Sausages

Story by Beverley Randell
Illustrated by Ernest Papps

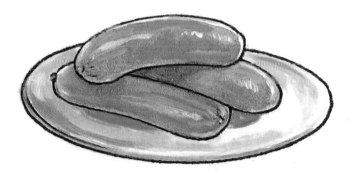

"Mum is asleep
and I am hungry,"
said Tom.

"Sh-sh-sh!" said Dad.

3

"The sausages are in here," said Tom.

"Here are the matches,"
said Tom.

"Thank you, Tom," said Dad.

"Look at the fire!"
said Tom.

"Here you are, Tom,"
said Dad.
"Here is a sausage
for you to cook."

"The sausages are cooking,"
said Tom.
"I am hungry."

"Here comes Mum,"
said Tom.

"Here is a sausage for you,"
said Dad.

"Thank you," said Mum.
"I am hungry, too."